The Northamptonshire Quiz Book

Kirby Hall

Mia Butler

Drawings by Helen Fenton

S.B. Publications

By the same author
Northamptonshire Rambles
Exploring the Nene Way
Secrets and Treasures of Northamptonshire
Let's Go Walkabout!

First published in 1997 by S.B.Publications
c/o 19 Grove Road, Seaford, East Sussex, BN25 1TP

ISBN 1 85770 136 4

Typeset by JEM Lewes and printed by
MPF Design and Print Ltd
32 Thomas Street, Longford Trading Estate,
Stretford, Greater Manchester M32 0JT

CONTENTS

Introduction		4
1	Countywide	5
2	Famous Men	6
3	The Arts	7
4	Castles	8
5	Famous Women	9
6	Dialect	10
7	Religious types	11
8	Miscellaneous	12
9	Industry	13
10	Sport	14
11	Waterways	15
12	Towns	16
13	Villages	17
14	Folklore	18
15	Buildings of Antiquity	19
16	Pubs	20
17	Enigmas	21
18	Royalty	22
19	Writers and Poets	23
20	Unnatural Causes	24
21	Rogues and Eccentrics	25
22	Fur and Feather	26
23	Churches	27
24	Battles and Skirmishes	28
25	Monuments	29
26	Heraldry	30
27	Railways	31
28	Museums	32
Picture Quiz		33
Answers		46

Front Cover: Where is this church? Back cover: Name this folly

INTRODUCTION

WHAT a bewildering multiplicity of choices —the discoveries are never ending. Fortunately, my inquisitive nature has led me to nose around my home county over the years, to my heart's delight, and wallow in its bounty.

However, readers would be well advised to imbibe some of the legends with a degree of licence. Remember, some of these tales, facts and figures, may have been somewhat embellished, or may even have 'variations on a theme', vague in the mists of time.

Perhaps you will browse through the book on winter nights, tax your memories, submit to intrigue, flex those muscles in summer and go and see for yourselves.

Otherwise, simply throw down the gauntlet and challenge the know-how of your friends and neighbours. Either way — enjoy!

Mia Butler

ACKNOWLEDGMENTS

Gratitude and garlands, for considerable input, to Marian Pipe and Colin Eaton — by whom I was aided and abetted several times over.

1 COUNTYWIDE

'The dumpling hills of Northamptonshire' — *Horace Walpole, historian*

1 Where is the county's highest point?
2 Which is the county's longest parish church?
3 Where is Armada House?
4 What is the Lutine Bell and what is the local connection?
5 Name two surviving tollhouses.
6 Which is thought to be the largest village green in the county?
7 The Nene Way is a long-distance footpath along the river valley. Where does it begin and end?
8 Where is there an isolated church tower, recognised as a landmark by the R.A.F.?
9 Where might you find Marble Arch, Pimlico, Potato Hall and Amen Place?
10 Why is Merry Tom Lane in Chapel Brampton so called?

Answers: Page 46

2 FAMOUS MEN

'No shire within this lande is so plentifully stored with Gentry' — *JN Norden, A Delineation of Northamptonshire*

1 This composer has written, among other works, the film score for Bridge over the River Kwai.
2 One of the knights who murdered Thomas a Becket and owned lands at Bulwick.
3 Who wrote the first definitive history of the county?
4 He started his working life as a baker's boy but rose dramatically to become Archbishop of Canterbury.
5 Northampton has elected many MPs over the centuries, but only one was to become Prime Minister, the only Prime Minister to be assasinated in office. Who was he?
6 Coco the Clown, who was Russian-born, lived in the county. Where?
7 Seen frequently on TV as a member of the 'Call My Bluff' team, he was also a tutor at Oundle School.
8 This county baronet was a Shakespearean actor, whose career began when he was at Oxford. Later, he appeared at The Old Vic, Sadlers Wells and Stratford.
9 Who was James Abram Garfield and what was his connection with the county?
10 Who founded schools in Oundle, Brigstock, Barnwell and Weekley and hospitals at Barnwell and Weekley?

Answers: Page 46

3 THE ARTS

'If Warkton were a hundred miles away they would go to see it' — *Sir Alfred East, painter*

1　Two brothers, highly acclaimed as author and architect.

2　Which famous film star trained at the Northampton Repertory Theatre in his early years?

3　In which religious place would you find Henry Moore's Madonna (1974) and Graham Sutherland's Crucifixion (1946)?

4　An internationally acknowledged artist, noted for his fine landscapes, is commemorated by an art gallery.

5　A barber by trade, he loved the countryside, was a member of a choral society, published 5 volumes of poetry and a book, as well as being a talented artist.

6　Soldier and diplomat, also highly respected as a musician and as a founder of The Royal Academy of Music.

7　Splendid monuments by the sculptor Roubillac of John, Duke of Montagu and Mary, Duchess of Montagu, repose here (1752 and 1753).

8　A Northampton-born musician played the violin for State Balls at Buckingham Palace for George V and Queen Mary between 1912 and 1913.

9　Artist and schoolmaster who lived in Scaldwell and was renowned for his pictures of important county buildings.

10　Sir Adrian Boult said of this composer 'he goes on creating masterpieces which I am convinced will survive their composer and most of those who are his contemporaries'.

Answers: Page 47

4 CASTLES

'This castle has a pleasant seat' —
William Shakespeare, Macbeth

1 This castle was originally built by William the Conqueror in the 11th century. In which TV series did it feature?

2 Mary, Queen of Scots, was beheaded in this riverside castle in 1587.

3 Which castle mound is a County Heritage Site, and said to be ringwork from King Stephen's reign of the 12th century?

4 A few stones on a rise are all that remain of this important stronghold, built by Simon de Senlis in the latter part of the 11th century.

5 Which castle is said to have been contructed by the de Quincy family, later to become the Earls of Winchester, who occupied the manor in the 12th and 13th century?

6 Where was Castle Hymel situated?

7 Was there ever a castle at Castle Ashby?

8 Formerly a 15th century manor house, only the tower and angular remnants have survived, with later additions. It is now a private house, to view only.

9 Little trace may be seen on the site of a castle demolished about 1633, beside the River Jordan, now only defined by vague earthworks.

10 A tennis court has been laid out within the walls of this castle.

Answers: Page 47

5 FAMOUS WOMEN

'She that is born a beauty is half married' — *Proverb, T Fuller, 1732*

1 Who was secretly married to Edward I on May 1, 1464, at Grafton Regis?
2 This lady took Queen Victoria's son, Leopold, to Europe, to improve his health. Whilst they were away the boy's father died.
3 For what was Hannah Burke remembered?
4 Which Northampton-born actress achieved fame in the Miss Marples series just before her retirement?
5 Which local woman was responsible for the establishment of the County Records Office and Northamptonshire Record Society.
6 Daughter of one of the richest men in the county, who gave Abington Park to the people of Northampton.
7 For many years this woman was the 'stand-in' for Elizabeth II at rehearsals for Trooping the Colour.
8 A woman of great age who lived through the reign of six sovereigns from Elizabeth I toWilliam and Mary.
9 The patron saint of lacemakers, condemned in 310 AD for her religious beliefs, she was lashed to a spiked wheel and when the wheel broke, she was beheaded; a firework bears her name.
10 America's first female poet, thought to have been born in Yardley Hastings.

Answers: Page 48

6 DIALECT

English as she is spoken — *anon*

1 To crumble into small pieces.
2 How does one 'hotchel'?
3 An evil spirit who drags travellers into the river.
4 Another name for a ladybird.
5 Who was labelled a 'barley bump'?
6 Describes an extremely perverse person.
7 What does this mean: 'Stick with yr 'oggin, if your a piggin'?
8 A pettichap.
9 To slibber.
10 A trolley-mog.

Answers: Page 48

7 RELIGIOUS TYPES

'An you've got to git up airly ef you want to take in God' — *James Russell Lowell (1819-1891), The Biglow Papers*

1 Co-founder of the Baptist Missionary Society in 1792, William Carey was pastor here and married Dorothy Plackett in 1781.
2 On July 2, 1643, 12 Parliamentary troopers tried to arrest the vicar, William Losse, at his church. He fled into the belfry, was wounded and left for dead. Where did this incident occur?
3 Relics of Doctor David Livingstone are to be found here and the carved choir stalls reflect his work as a missionary.
4 Who is thought to have founded the first Sunday School in this county?
5 Co-founder and first secretary of the Baptist Missionary Society, until his death in 1815.
6 Who wrote the hymn O happy Day, part of which was to become a chart-topping song?
7 Harry Whittaker was appointed to expand which newly-formed association in 1961?
8 Who flouted the authority of his benefactor and landowner by declaring himself 'Dr, JP, Quorum and Parson'?
9 John Bunyan and John Wesley are said to have preached beneath a now somewhat dilapidated tree in this village.
10 This man was the Rector of St. Marys in Rushden between 1868 and 1890. He restored the church, built an infants school and a Mission room and school at the foot of Rushden Hill. He was also largely responsible for the National School which opened in 1870.

Answers: Page 49

8 MISCELLANEOUS

DUCKS & CHILDREN CROSSING

'O, it's a snug little island: A right little, tight little island' — *Thomas Dibdin (1771-1841)*

1 William Baucutt was confined here for drunkeness and ill-treating his spouse, about 100 years ago.

2 Joseph Merrick, a hideously disfigured man, spent secret holidays on Lady Knightley's Fawsley estates. By what name was he commonly known?

3 Which church is the keeper of a vamping-horn, one of only two surviving in this county?

4 What is a potence and where might you find one?

5 Where are two heads better than a hanging-basket?

6 Oliver Cromwell is said to have had his shoes made here.

7 Where to see a 'columbarium'?

8 Although primarily noted for his tremendous strength, he was reputed to have had five wives and thirty-three children.

9 High Sheriff Philip Agnew JP used to be the principal proprietor and editor of Punch magazine. Of which village was he a resident?

10 The Sir Henry Royce Memorial Foundation and Rolls Royce Enthusiasts Club are based in this county. Where?

Answers: Page 49

9 INDUSTRY

'Northampton, the county of beautiful bobbins' —
celebrating lacemaking

1 What does PLUTO represent?
2 Charles Wicksteed, a local benefactor, made his name in industrial engineering and consequently made a generous gift to the people of this town.
3 Where and what was Wembley Pit?
4 These business premises have become known as 'The Lighthouse'.
5 Famous slate for roofing tiles was quarried in this locality from the 14th century to 1967 and took its name from the nearby village.
6 A Danish company opened its busines premises on a site settled by a Danish community in the 9th century.
7 Now in use as a working men's club, this building was formerly a factory making horse collars, saddles and matting, utilising rushes from the river banks.
8 Clickers, closers, rough stuff men, last men and finishers, are terms of which trade?
9 What was LIBER CUSTUMARUM?
10 Who organised a protest march, following a slump in the manufacture of army boots after the Boer War, from Raunds to the War Office in London in 1905?

Answers: Page 50

10 SPORT

'Sport is sweetest when there are no spectators' — *J Clarke, proverb 1639*

1 No racing on this racecourse.
2 Where is there a memorial plaque to an admired horse, out in the country?
3 A former RAF station which currently hosts a World Championship series.
4 Who are the Poppies, the Cobblers, the Steelmen and the Diamonds?
5 An important annual event draws competitors and fans to the hamlet of Little Everdon.
6 Where do folk 'go conkers' every year, in October?
7 A Gothic style cross in this market place salutes a local solicitor, Clerk to the County Magistrates and worthy sportsman. He was the winner of the National Hunt Steeplechase run at Market Harborough on Bridegroom in 1860 and again the following year on 'Queensferry'.
8 On Cow Meadow (now Beckets Park) Northampton in 1741, the earliest game of its kind took place between two counties.
9 Winner of the Grand Prix at Silverstone in 1976, with a county connection.
10 For many years, a former MP and peer of the realm, was Master of the Pytchley Hunt.

Answers: Page 50

11 WATERWAYS

'Yet my great-grand
father was but a water-
man, looking one way,
rowing another: I got
most of my estate by the
same occupation' —
*John Bunyan, Pilgrims
Progress 1678*

1   The longest navigable canal in the county.
2   Where is there a designated Ancient Bridge over the River Jordan?
3   How many working mills are there left on the River Nene?
4   Where is Simsey Island?
5   A bridge over the Ise Brook is assumed to have borne the funeral cortege of Queen Eleanor, wife of Edward I, in 1290. Which one?
6   What is the 'Iron Trunk'?
7   About which water can you sail, fish, horse-ride, birdwatch, walk the perimeter and visit a nature reserve designated SSSI (Site of Special Scientific Interest)?
8   What is a 'cattle-creep'?
9   To what did this bequest refer? 'I bequest... a heyffor of 5 years with a white baby'?
10 The River Welland rises in the cellar of this vicarage.

Answers: Page 51

12 TOWNS

'The handsomest and best built town in all of England' — *Daniel Defoe (1661-1731), referring to Northampton*

1 This town was known as Lactodorum in Roman times.
2 By what names are Artleborough and Rowell better known?
3 These ancient spellings, 'Deresburg' (1086) and 'Deresburc' (1166), refer to which town?
4 The first radio transmitter was opened on this site in 1926, to become redundant in 1995.
5 King John, in 1204, granted a Charter for an annual week-long street fair here, still carried on today.
6 With which towns are the following twinned? Northampton, Higham Ferrers, Irchester and Daventry?
7 In 1227, King Henry granted a Charter to the Abbot of Peterborough for a weekly market to run '... for ever, well and in peace'. Where?
8 What was the function of a Moot Hall and where is there one?
9 The following wells relate specifically to which town? Red, Stone, Lady, Whyte, Holy and Hemming.
10 Where was saffron, used in cooking and for dyeing purposes, known to be grown?

Answers: Page 52

13 VILLAGES

'If you would be known and not know, vegetate in a village; if you would know and not be known, live in a city' — *CC Colton*

1 These villages are linked, but in what way? Middleton Cheney, Chacombe and Upper and Lower Wardington.
2 What is and where to find a 'jo stone'?
3 A churchyard known as 'God's Little Acre' and thought to be the venue for Thomas Gray's Elegy, rather than Stoke Poges.
4 An isolated altar stone remains in the middle of a field, after the deconsecration and demolition of the former church.
5 A deserted village with a sleepy sounding name.
6 Which village is noted for the fruit trees, originally cultivated 4,000 years ago in China, along the street?
7 The first village school built by Northants County Council, after education in the county was transferred to it under the Act of 1902.
8 What do these places have in comnon? Upper Boddington, Aston-le-Walls and Byfield.
9 Which village residents are known as 'Barton Leeks'?
10 What is the significance of 'Charlie's Pebble' and where is it?

Answers: Page 52

14 FOLKLORE

'Old faces glimmered
through the doors, old
footsteps trod the upper
floors' — *Tennyson,
Mariana (1809-1892)*

1 Who was Skulking Dudley?
2 Which village has a Tin Can Band?
3 What is the Bocase Stone?
4 What was Jack the Fiddlers claim to notoriety?
5 What was the 'miracle of the geese'?
6 What tale is told in 'The Mistletoe Bough'?
7 Why is the hamlet of Stowe Nine Churches so called?
8 For what was Jack of Badsaddle knighted?
9 How is the Dun Cow remembered?
10 Who is Stone Moses?

Answers: Page 53

15 BUILDINGS OF ANTIQUITY

'Building is a sweet impoverishing' — *G Herbert, proverb from the 17th century*

1 Which house was the ancestral home of the first US President?
2 Memorabilia here includes the head of charger Roland, ridden by the 7th Earl of Cardigan, at the Charge of the Light Brigade during the Battle of Balaclava.
3 This stately home has seven courtyards, 52 chimney-stacks, 365 windows and a deer leap in the boundary wall:
4 At which two houses was Charles I allowed to play bowls whilst being held prisoner at Holdenby House in 1647?
5 Which is the largest dovecote in England?
6 A unique building symbolising the Holy Trinity.
7 The first garden gnome was brought to this house from Nuremberg by Sir Charles Isham for his rock garden.
8 This house, begun in 1570 by Sir Humphrey Stafford and completed by Sir Christopher Hatton has been partially restored after near dereliction.
9 Which house, now in the care of the National Trust, was the home of the Dryden family since the 16th century?
10 The skeleton of an incomplete lodge remains unroofed. It was begun by Sir thomas Tresham in 1595 and follows a religious form with a wealth of inscriptons.
Answers: Page 54

16 PUBS

'He is an ill guest who never drinks to his host' — *J Ray, proverb 1670*

1 What is unique about The Ten O'Clock pub at Little Harrowden?
2 Why is The World's End at Ecton so called?
3 Name two coaching inns in the county.
4 Which Duke gave his name to The Duke's Head at Deanshanger?
5 Where is and why The World Upside Down pub?
6 The oldest licensed premises in Northamptonshire.
7 A 'man of the cloth' purchased The Tollemache Arms at Harrington. For what reason?
8 How did 'The Haycock at Wansford get its name?
9 What is celebrated by The Duke of Wellington at Stanwick?
10 This pub, a listed building, can boast a fireplace, brought from Fotheringhay Castle, after it was razed to the ground, following the execution there of Mary Queen of Scots in 1587.

Answers: Page 55

17 ENIGMAS

'You throw the sand against the wind
  And the wind blows it back again'
— *William Blake, Voltaire*

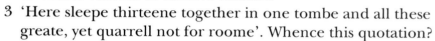

1 An isolated church has been converted to a popular field centre, where the graveyard remains consecrated ground.
2 A 200 year old dilapidated windmill has been revamped, to enable viewers to observe wildlife.
3 'Here sleepe thirteene together in one tombe and all these greate, yet quarrell not for roome'. Whence this quotation?
4 At Michaelmas 1380, the men of Doddington were 'amerced' the sum of 6s 8p for default. In what respect?
5 Where is there a church spire that is set beside the tower?
6 A 'learned physician' made this astonishing claim '.. it fastens the teeth though ready to drop out' in 1488. To what does it refer?
7 An isolated tower in a public park, of 1678, where the well was serviced by a waterwheel, with stairs to the dovecote above.
8 Where would you find the following famous men grouped together under one roof ? Winston Churchill, Franklin Roosevelt, John Cabot, the Pilgrim Fathers, Thomas Hooker, William Penn and Abraham Lincoln.
9 Village known of old as 'Pudding Bag Marston'.
10 Does a 'kissing-gate' suggest you stop to kiss?

Answers: Page 56

21

18 ROYALTY

'Kings and beasts very often worry their keepers' — *D Fergusson, Scottish proverb 1641*

1 Richard the Lionheart sometimes stayed here prior to joining the Crusades to the Holy Land.
2 One of the wives of Henry VIII had a father who was lord of the manor of Greens Norton.
3 Richard III was born at this castle to parents Richard Plantagenet and Cicely Neville, Duke and Duchess of York, in 1452.
4 Charles I and his queen came here to take the waters in 1628 and stayed at The White Swan Inn.
5 Who did Edward IV meet under an oak tree in Whittlewood Forest in 1464, fall in love with, and marry?
6 Which former royal favourite was beheaded on August 25 1485, but the cross on his grave slab states that he died on August 20?
7 Where would you find a market cross listing all the kings and queens of England between 1586 and 1887?
8 Which monarch donated 1,000 tons of timber from royal forests to Northampton in 1675?
9 Queen Boadicea, who died in AD62, could possibly be buried in which village.
10 The ghost of this queen is said to haunt the staircase of a hotel in a famous scholarly town.

Answers: Page 56

19 WRITERS AND POETS

'There is a great deal of difference between the eager man, who wants to read a book and the tired man who wants a book to read' — *Charles Dickens*

1 An author of much sporting history who donated the royalties from his novels to good causes.
2 Born in 1631 of Puritan parents, he was to become Poet Laureate.
3 A talented family trio of poets and writers.
4 Why would Flora Thompson have a drive named for her?
5 Which famous author was a frequent visitor to Rockingham Castle in the last century?
6 This man's books for the country-lover included *The Quiet Fields*, *Tides Turning* and *Little Grey Men*.
7 Born in Rushden in 1905, he wrote *Love for Lydia*, based on a local setting, and was awarded a CBE in 1973.
8 An acknowledged county poet, he was a mental patient at the town's hospital and frequently wandered the riverside.
9 This writer, born at Newnham near Daventry in 1605, was viewed as a possible successor to William Shakespeare.
10 His family came to England from Holland in the 18th century. He started work as a secretary at the Colonial Office in London. Later he became editor of *The Northampton Mercury*.

Answers: Page 57

20 UNNATURAL CAUSES

'When we want to read of the dead that are down to love, whither do we turn? To the murder column' — *GB Shaw, Three Plays for a Puritan*

1 In 1686, following an energetic chase, the local butcher murdered his wife's lover, at Wappenham. Who was he?
2 A highwayman hanged at the time of the annual horse-fair in 1826.
3 A headstone, face to the wall in a churchyard, records the drowning of a black servant while trying to rescue his master from a lake in June 1838. Who and where?
4 Whilst awaiting trial for murder, this man committed suicide and was buried in 'Knitters grave'.
5 Who and when were the last witches executed in the county?
6 Which horse, winner of the 1884 Derby, was butchered and buried following a lawsuit challenging its age.
7 Which two poachers were hanged at the gallows in 1748, for stealing deer from Whittlebury Forest.
8 An attendant of Henrietta Maria, wife of Charles I, this young woman secretly loved the monarch's messenger, who was murdered by a jealous courtier. Who was she?
9 Which brother and sister both died as a result of their religious beliefs, opposing local opinion, in 1641.
10 Who was accused of murdering a young woman and her baby, in a bacon warehouse in Dychurch Lane, Northampton in 1892?
Answers: Page 57

21 ROGUES AND ECCENTRICS

'It is the very error of the Moon: she comes more nearer Earth than she wont and makes men mad' —
Shakespeare, Othello, Act V

1 Which co-conspirator of the Gunpowder Plot in 1605 lived in the county?

2 Which farmer had his dead wife and daughter bricked up in an outhouse before his own death in 1861?

3 Harry Wood was an 'inspector of milestones', but known by a nickname and had a pub named after him.

4 In which village did the lord of the manor lay a 15 inch guage steam railway in 1903?

5 Where did the late 18th century Culworth Gang of highway robbers and burglars store much of' their booty?

6 A vicar's Will of 1783 directed that his body remain in his bed until it 'became offensive' and then carried to his summerhouse where entrances were to be barred. Where?

7 Who was the prodigious walker, born at Woodford in 1764, who covered 1,100 miles in 1,100 hours?

8 Who made a fortune in Russia by piracy and was executed in Moscow in 1612?.

9 Three young men caught poaching left the gamekeeper dying from their gunshot. They were later arrested. Where did the incident occur and what became of the miscreants?

10 What episode became known as the 'Blazing Car Mystery'?

Answers: Page 58

22 FUR AND FEATHER

'Wee fleeket, cowran, tim'rous beastie'
— *Robert Burns (1759-1796)*

1 Who introduced Little Owls into this country?
2 Name the 1901 winner of the Grand National whose hooves were buttered to gain advantage over the other runners on a snowy racecourse.
3 Where is there a poignant statue of a much-loved dog?
4 Where would you find a redundant sheep-wash?
5 Which country gentleman brought Pere David deer (or Milu), natives of China, into his estate?
6 Shagfoals, shucks and padfoots - what are they?
7 This lady was known for her kindness to animals and planted an avenue of cherry trees for the birds on her family estate.
8 Which village library has a pair of quaint iron duck heads protruding from the front wall?
9 Congyre, cunniger or conygher - what would this name signify?
10 During the Civil War Parliamentary soldiers arrested the Royalist Vicar of Wellingborough. On the march to Northampton, he was forced to ride on the back of an animal. Who was he and on what creature did he travel?

Answers: Page 59

23 CHURCHES

**'If anybody calls, say I am design-
ing St. Pauls'** — *Christopher Wren*

1 A church noted for its
   strainer arch, curved both at
   the top and the bottom.
2 Which is 'the oldest church
   north of the Alps'?
3 What is a 'sheila-na-gig' and
   where to see one?
4 This church has floor tiles of
   green and gold, designed by
   Lord Alwyne Compton, Bishop of Ely.
5 Where is there a 'much cross-legged' knight c 1300,
   thought to be a memorial to William de Ros, who died on a
   pilgrimage to the Holy Land in 1352?
6 Stored in which crypt are the skulls and thighbones of 1500
   individuals?
7 Name two churches with scratch or mass dials?
8 Where can the bride for marriage, nor the corpse for bur-
   ial, not be brought to the church by motor vehicle?
9 Where, in this county, is the only original round church situated?
10 What is enclosed in a glass fronted case, within a pillar of
   the nave of the parish church of St Mary the Virgin, at
   Woodford?

Answers: Page 59

24 BATTLES AND SKIRMISHES

'His cause is just who gets his blow in fust' - *anon*

1 Oliver Cromwell is said to have tethered his horse on the eve of the Battle of Naseby in this place.
2 Defeated at the Battle of Naseby, King Charles I was later held prisoner here between February and June 1647.
3 'The Levellers' were a body of peasants led by 'Captain Pouch' who revolted when wealthy landlords enclosed their pastures for widespread sheep farming. What was their fate?
4 Built for the protection of the monarch at a place considered to be the furthest point inland from the coast, in the event of a battle that failed to materialise.
5 Where is Vigo Lodge, named after the British naval victory at Vigo, Spain in 1702?
6 A woodland taking the name of a battle of 1815.
7 The Battle of Northampton raged on July 10, 1460, but where did the action actually take place?
8 Which village suffered casualties in the Civil War, when Thomas Winkles and Henry Balfour were killed on August 9, 1642?
9 Which castle was captured from the Royalists in 1643 and occupied by the Roundheads, during the Civil War?
10 Which church door was blown open with a petard when Royalist soldiers stormed the building in order to capture a party of fifty Roundhead soldiers who were locked inside?

Answers: Page 60

25 MONUMENTS

'He was not of an age, but for all time' — *anon*

1 It is recorded that William of Ireland was paid the sum of £3 6s 8d for each statue he carved of the queen. On which monument was this?
2 'A good man, a gallant soldier, a true sportsman' is inscribed on this memorial at Pitsford. To whom does it refer?
3 Which monument marks the assumed place where Cromwell led the cavalry charge in a momentous battle.
4 Who erected a modest pyramid obelisk at a crossroads 'to record the many blessings of 1798'?
5 Who was the radical MP for Northampton who was the first atheist to sit in the House of Commons?
6 This man died in a flying accident in 1899 and his monument stands in the grounds of Stanford Hall.
7 A tribute to rugby player Edgar Mobbs, killed in the Great War in 1917, now stands in front of the War Memorial in Abington Square. Where was it previously sited?
8 Where is there an obelisk dedicated to the Duke of Devonshire, and who built it?,
9 A circular tower was erected to commemorate a certain battle following a chance remark by the Duke of Wellington. Where is it and what does it signify?
10 To whom is a granite stone on the A427, between Weldon and Benefield, inscribed 'The Best Damned Outfit in the USAAF' dedicated?

Answers: Page 60

26 HERALDRY

'The boast of heraldry, the pomp of power,
And all that beauty, all that wealth, e'er gave,
Awaits th'inevitable hour,
The path of glory leads but to the grave' — *Thomas Gray, 1751*

1 Which town coat of arms portrays five wells and springs?
2 This family's heraldic shield is said to have been the design behind the American flag.
3 The motto beneath Northampton's coat of arms reads 'castello fortior concordia'. What is the translation?
4 The Spencer family of Althorp has two armorial bearings. The one normally used consists of frets and scallop shells. What is featured on the other?
5 What animals appear on Northamptonshire's coat of arms?
6 Who does the figure of a negro on Kettering's coat of arms represent?
7 The Abbey of James at Northampton, which was swept away after the Reformation, had which object on its shield?
8 Diamond-shaped hatchments, which came into vogue in the early 17th century but are seldom used nowadays, are usually found where?
9 In which church is the oldest painted royal arms?
10 What are the three identical items of protective clothing on the shield of the Brudenell family of Deene Hall?

Answers: Page 61

27 RAILWAYS

'Railway termini.
They are our gates to the glorious and
  unknown,
Thru them we pass out into adventure
  and sunshine,
To them alas: we return.' — *EM Forster*

1 Where to go for a 'Santa Special' and other recreational trips?
2 Six people were killed and many injured in a railway disaster in September 1898; on which line?
3 This construction took three years to build, is three quarters of a mile long, involved hundreds of navvies, hordes of horses and millions of bricks.
4 Which railway station had the least use of any in the county?
5 Which Station Master was responsible for the annual supply of 20lb of walnuts to the St Pancras Hotel at the terminus in London?
6 A mile of disused rail line is now incorporated into a recognised Town Walk. Where?
7 At one time, this was the longest tunnel of the Victorian era on the London to Birmingham line.
8 Where may relics from ironstone railways be seen?
9 What was the major item of freight carried on the Stratford-on-Avon, Towcester-Olney line?
10 Which was the last railway line to be built in this county?

Answers: Page 62

28 MUSEUMS

'The stacking together of the paintings of the masters in museums is a catastrophe, And a collection of a hundred good intellects produces collectively one idiot.' — *CG Jung*

1 Europe's only Dragonfly Museum and Sanctuary.
2 Working models and industrial exhibits featuring 'The Story of Steel' may be seen at this location.
3 A collection of examples of lace-making and early local industries are shown together in this gathering of artifacts.
4 Comprehensive displays depicting 200 years of canal life are housed in this restored cornmill.
5 Elizabeth Bernard, Shakespeare's grand-daughter, once lived in this mansion.
6 Memorabilia devoted to aviation and airfields of World War II is on show here.
7 A huge replica boot, as worn by an elephant in a re-enactment of Hannibal's crossing of the Alps, is on display here.
8 A reed instrument originally attributed to Kratzenstein in Copenhagen about 1779, is one of the many fascinating items here.
9 Where and what is Jim Crow?
10 Which elaborate example of Celtic art, found in this county, is now in The British Museum?

Answers: Page 62

PICTURE QUIZ

Test your local knowledge on
buildings and objects
familiar and unfamiliar

Answers: Page 63

1 The remains of a fine columbarium - where?

2 What is this, and who built it?

3 Where is this strange triangular building?

4 Locally known as the Greek Archer; where is this statue?

5 Name this viaduct across the Welland Valley

6 This is said to be the oldest church north of the Alps

7 Where is this wattle and daub wall?

8 Piles of bones; shelves of skulls. Where?

9 What is this, and where can it be found?

10 Where is this late Elizabethan dovecote?

11 In which town is this well located?

13 Right,
on which
church is
this
striking
blue
clock?

12 Left, where is this Roman
coffin lid to be found?

14 What , and where is this strange horn?

15 The village stocks - where?

16 In which village is this attractive pump?

17 Swan gates at Lamport Hall, emblem of which family?

18 Where is this lift bridge over the Grand Union Canal?

19 For what was this Jim Crow tool used?

20 Where is this extraordinary market cross?

THE ANSWERS

1 COUNTYWIDE

1 Arbury Hill, near Daventry, at 734ft.
2 Holy Trinity church, Rothwell.
3 Weston-by-Weedon, the house is dated 1588, the year of the Spanish Armada.
4 The Lutine Bell, now in Lloyds of London, is rung to precede a significant announcement, such as a disaster at sea. The bell is in memory of the son of a former vicar of Easton-on-the-Hill, Lancelot Skinner, who perished when his ship, *La Lutine*, was lost off the coast of Holland in 1799, where the artifact was recovered.
5 Sudborough and Twywell.
6 Nether Heyford, of about 5 acres.
7 Badby and Wansford.
8 St Peter's church, Little Brington.
9 Northampton, Brackley, Wellingborough and Little Addington.
10 It is said that Earl Spencer's favourite hunter, Merry Tom, was killed jumping the brook nearby, and the Earl ordered that the horse be buried there complete with saddle and bridle.

2 FAMOUS MEN

1 Sir Malcolm Arnold.
2 Reginald Fitzurse.
3 John Bridges, County Historian, His book was published in 1791, but it is incomplete.
4 Henry Chichelle, born 1362, in Higham Ferrers.
5 Spencer Percival.
6 At Woodnewton, where Nicholai Polakovs OBE (1900-1974) is buried in the graveyard of St Marys church.
7 Arthur Marshall.
8 Sir Gyles Isham of Lamport Hall.

9   He was 20th President of the United States, born at Ashby St
    Ledgers in 1831.
10 The Rev Nicholas Latham.

3 THE ARTS

1   Thomas Cooper Gotch and John Alfred Gotch.
2   Errol Flynn.
3   St. Matthew's church, Northampton. Both were commissioned by
    The Reverend Walter Hussey.
4   Sir Alfred East RA, in the Alfred East Art Gallery by JA Gotch, of
    Kettering, 1913.
5   George Harrison of Kettering, 1876-1950. His book *A Wanderer in
    Northamptonshire* was published in 1946.
6   John Fane, 11th Earl of Westmorland (1784-1858), whose family
    seat was Apethorpe Hall.
7   St Edmund's church, Warkton.
8   Frederick Stock.
9   George Clark, died 1868.
10 Edmund Rubbra.

4 CASTLES

1   'By the Sword Divided' was filmed on location at Rockingham
    Castle.
2   The Queen was executed in the Banqueting Hall of Fotheringhay
    Castle.
3   Culworth Castle.
4   Northampton Castle.
5   Long Buckby castle, where the site is now a Pocket Park and
    County Heritage Site (allowing public access to earthworks).
6   Fineshade Abbey (off the A43 to Stamford). On the site of an
    Augustinian Priory destroyed in 1749, prior to the early
    monastery of the 13th century

7 Yes. The 11th century ruins were beneath the foundations of the present Elizabethan mansion, Castle Ashby House, from 1574.
8 Astwell Manor, Helmdon.
9 Braybrooke Castle.
10 Barnwell Castle.

5 FAMOUS WOMEN

1 Elizabeth Woodville, who was eventually crowned Queen in Westminster Abbey in May 1465. She was to become the mother of the Princes murdered in the Tower of London.
2 Louisa Mary Bowater, later to become Lady Knightley of Fawsley.
3 During the Great Fire of Wellingborough in 1748 she poured beer on to the thatched roof of her cottage and saved it.
4 Joan Hickson.
5 Miss Joan Wake (1884-1974).
6 Lady Wantage, whose father was the first and last Lord Overstone.
7 Sylvia Stainer of Maidwell.
8 Information recorded on the gravestone of Alice Old in Weedon Bec churchyard.
9 St Katharine of Alexandria, to whom the church at Irchester is dedicated, whose Saints Day is November 25th.
10 Ann Bradstreet, 1612-1672.

6 DIALECT

1 Crimble.
2 Move in a bobbing manner.
3 Jimmy Buntail.
4 A ladylock.
5 A lazy person.
6 Ornithwrinkle.
7 'Don't change your plan'.
8 Another name for a long-tailed titmouse.
9 To slide or stumble.

10   A grimy or disorderly person.

7 RELIGIOUS TYPES

1   At Moulton.
2   St Marys church at Weedon Lois.
3   St Nicholas church, Twywell.
4   Thomas Jones at Creaton in 1789.
5   Andrew Fuller.
6   Philip Doddridge.
7   The Northamptonshire Association of Youth Clubs.
8   Dr John Williams in 1618, whose parsonage was at Grafton
    Underwood, when villagers were forbidden to sell ale or
    encourage entertainers from outsiders, at their annual fair, by
    a Warrant. His opposition was to Edward Montagu of Boughton
    House. Dr Williams went on to become Dean of Salisbury and
    ultimately, Archbishop of York.
9   At Easton Maudit.
10   John Thomas Parker (1826-1890).

8 MISCELLANEOUS

1   In the stocks at Little Houghton.
2   The Elephant Man.
3.   The church of St Peter and St Paul at Harrington. Purported to
    be an ancient wind instriunent used to encourage the choir to
    greater effect or as a loudspeaker.
4   It is the central pole with a ladder attachment which swings round
    to access nest-boxes, in a dovecote as at Wadenhoe (a County
    Heritage site).
5   On the butcher's shop at Little Houghton. Clever sheet metal
    heads of a ram and a bull.
6   Walgrave.
7   Retaining wall of a dovecote on the edge of the school playing-
    field at Wilbarston. (County Heritage site but requiring

49

permission from the primary school office during term time).

8   John Smart of Kettering, who died in 1774.
9   Farthingstone.
10   Paulerspury

9 INDUSTRY

1   Pipe Line Under The Ocean, through which fuel was pumped beneath the English Channel for the allied troops during World War II. The pipes were manufactured at Corby Steel Works.
2   Wicksteed Park at Kettering, opened in 1921, and continues to attract visitors from all over the country.
3   The Pit is now a feature of Irchester Country Park, where the former ironstone quarry remains as a craggy outcrop of natural history.
4   Formerly the Express Lift Tower of 418ft at Northampton.
5   Collyweston, near Stamford.
6   Carlsberg Brewery, Northampton.
7   The factory at Islip was handy for the gathering of rushes from the banks of the River Nene.
8   The footwear trade, which was an essential industry from 1642 onwards.
9   A Book of Customs of Northampton, recording the trading regulations of various industries such as livery compenies, shoemakers, fullers and weavers etc, from about 1430.
10   James Gribble, an ex-soldier dubbed the 'General', when the trade revived.

10 SPORT

1   The Racecourse, in the county town, is a recreational facility.
2   At Upper Harlestone Sports Field, where Cotherstone is buried. He won the 2,000 Guineas and the 1843 Derby, among other races. His final owner was Lord Spencer of Althorp.
3   Silverstone International Circuit.

4   They are football teams from Kettering, Northampton, Corby and
    Rushden.
5   The Everdon Horse Trials.
6   On Ashton village green, near Oundle, at the World Conker
    Championship.
7   The monument, at Daventry, is to Edmund Charles Burton.
8   A game of cricket between Northamptonshire and
    Huntingdonshire.
9   James Hunt drove a Hesketh racing car, backed by Lord Hesketh
    of Easton Neston.
10 Lord Paget, formerly Reggie Paget.

11 WATERWAYS

1   Blisworth Tunnel at 3075 yards long, on the Grand Union Canal.
2   At Braybrooke, built by Sir Thomas de Latymer in 1401-2.
3   Two, at Bugbrooke and Wellingborough.
4   A small, privately owned plot, in the River Nene at Wansford.
5   The ancient bridge at Geddington.
6   It is an aqueduct, near to Cosgrove, carrying the Grand Union
    Canal over the River Great Ouse, the county boundary between
    Northamptonshire and Buckinghamshire.
7   Pitsford Reservoir. Permits available from The Lodge, Anglian
    Water, near Holcot.
8   A tunnel for pedestrians or cattle to pass under the canal. There
    are two such passages under the water at Cosgrove.
9   A passage from the Will of T Werwyke of 1540, referring to the
    upkeep of the medieval bridge at Kislingbury.
10 At Sibbertoft.

12 TOWNS

1   Towcester.
2   Irthlingborough and Rothwell.
3   Desborough.

4   At Borough Hill, Daventry.
5   Rothwell.
6   Poitiers and Marburg, Lorelei, Coulon and Westerburg.
7   Kettering.
8   In a Borough, incorporated by Royal Charter, the JPs met to administer government, such as at Daventry, though the building now housing a museum.
9   Some of the many wells at Wellingborough.
10 In the area of Saffron road, where there is a 'cup-and-saucer' moat and medieval fishponds, at Higham Ferrers.

13 VILLAGES

1   By the Jurassic Way, a recreational footpath of 88 miles from Banbury to Stamford.
2   It is a boulder stone, often placed to protect corner walls from cartwheel damage in the old days and sometimes used to 'seal a bargain' with a handshake over it.
3   St Marys church at Great Everdon.
4   Former site of the church of St Denys, of the deserted village of Faxton.
5   Snorscombe.
6   Aynho, noted for its apricot trees, given to the tenants by the Cartwright family, who were Lords of the Manor from 1615 until the 1950s.
7   Byfield in 1906.
8   Linked by an old drovers trackway, Welsh road, when these men herded cattle from Wales via Buckingham to the south of England.
9   Earls Barton, where an annual Leek Pie Supper is held on Shrove Tuesday.
10 A boulder set by the wall of the Manor House, used by Charles I to review his 10,000 troops en route to the Battle of Cropredy Bridge.
    His visit to the manor at Culworth is recorded in June 1644.

14 FOLKORE

1   Dudley, Lord of the Manor of Clopton, in 1349, fought a duel
    with his cousin, Sir Richard de Hazelbeere, over the rights to his
    property. He was the survivor, though not for long. His apparition
    became known as Skulking Dudley and was seen to wander the
    local environs. In 1905, the villagers asked the Bishop of
    Peterborough to exorcise the ghost and consequently, the Bishop
    and twenty-one clergymen proceeded with the ritual, when the
    spectre was laid to rest.

2   Broughton, where, at the end of November, the band and their
    followers parade through the streets making a din by banging tin
    cans and dustbin lids. The custom is aimed to drive out any evil
    spirits.

3   It is a large stone inscribed 'in this plaes grew Bocase Tree' and
    marks the site of a previous giant oak, in Harry's Park Wood at
    Brigstock. Legend has it that Robin Hood hid his bows and
    arrows in the trunk, when pursued by Sir Ralph de Harville and
    his followers, who were chasing the band of outlaws. Robin
    outwitted his enemies and rejoined his fellows to live another day:
    other tales, too, relate to this stone.

4   In the 17th century, Rushton Hall was thought to be connected to
    Triangular Lodge in the far side of the grounds, by a tunnel.
    Viscount Cullen, the owner, offered a reward of fifty guineas to
    one who would traverse the dark passage. Jack entered the lodge,
    playing his fiddle, whose strains gradually faded into the
    blackness. He was never seen again and the money was awarded
    to his apparently bereaved spouse, who very soon married again
    to a man who was the exact image of her husband!

5   Marauding geese had destroyed the villagers' crops, when St
    Werburgh of Weedon is said to have revived a dead goose, on the
    condition that they never came again. Since that time, history has
    not repeated itself and a stained glass window in St Peter's church
    illustrates this legend.

6   A young bride, Maud, maried Sir John Lovell at Titchmarsh
    Castle in medieval times, and ran off in her wedding finery in a
    game of hide and seek. She hid in an oak chest, pulling the heavy

lid shut and though the guests searched everywhere, she was never found. Many years later, a servant opened an ancient chest and discovered the skeleton of the missing maiden.

7　Eight times the holy man and his labourers strove to build a church in the valley, which each time was mysteriously razed. Finally, after a night of vigil, the ninth attempt began on the crest of the hill, where St Michael's has stood to this day.

8　A young forester, Jack, wandering in the woods, saved his monarch by slaying 'the last wild boar in England', after his horse was startled by the animal. In appreciation, the King elevated him on the spot, to Sir John de Wythmayle, whose alabaster effigy now lies in St Mary's Church at Orlingbury. Other versions of this tale also exist.

9　Supposedly, a much loved Dun Cow supplied the poor and needy of the parish of Stanion with unlimited milk. The local witch challenged this and wreaked her vengeance by tricking the villagers by placing a pail riddled with holes beneath the cow. The animal laboured but could not fill it and died from exhaustion. The huge rib, in the care of St Peter's Church, is said to be from the revered animal.

10　A statue in a copse just outside Weekley,. He is said to come down from his pedestal o drink at the nearby spring at the stroke of midnight. However, there is no striking clock at the village church.

15 BUILDINGS OF ANTIQUITY

1　Sulgrave Manor, purchased by Lawrence Washington in 1538, who was twice Mayor of Northampton.

2　Deene Hall, near Corby.

3　Boughton House, an estate of the Duke of Buccleugh.

4　Althorp and Boughton Hall, both near to Northampton.

5　At Newton, near to Geddington, built of limestone and containing 2,000 nest-boxes. It bears the name 'Maurice Tresham' (b 1530).

6　Triangular Lodge, in the grounds of Rushton Hall, built by Sir Thomas Tresham and completed in 1597, after his imprisonment

for his Catholic beliefs.
7   To Lamport Hall.
8   Kirby Hall, near Gretton, now administered by English Heritage.
9   Canons Ashby House, near Daventry, in the care of The National
    Trust.
10 Lyveden New Build, near Oundle, under the auspices of The
    National Trust.

16 PUBS

1   There is no other pub in England of that name.
2   Many men died in defeat after the battle of Naseby, trudging
    through the countryside and so this became their 'world's end'.
    The original pub sign was painted by Hogarth, who offered it in
    settlement of a debt.   ,
3   The Saracen's Head at Towcester and The Crown Hotel at
    Brackley.
4   The Duke of Cumberland, son of George III.
5   At Raunds, named after the absent-minded landlord, Silas
    Coggin, who could never remember where he kept anything.
6   The Bell Inn at Finedon.
7   The Reverend Hugh Tollemache, so that he could close the pub
    on Sundays.
8   From the story of Barnabas, visiting the village, who fell asleep on
    a haycock and was washed along by a sudden flood on the River
    Nene. Thinking that he had been washed out to sea, he asked
    those peering over the bridge where he might be. 'Wansford,'
    they replied. 'Wansford-in-England?' he asked.
9   The place where his famous Wellington Boots were made.
10 The Black Horse Inn at Nassington.

17 ENIGMAS

1   St Faith's Church at Newton-in-the-Willows.
2   Newnham Hill, near Daventry.

3　On a memorial tablet in the church of the Holy Trinity at Blatherwycke, to Thomas Randolph, poet, commissioned by Sir Christopher Hatton.

4　They were fined for the neglect of Hardwater Bridge, by the Jurors of the Higham Ferrers Hundred.

5　At the Church of the Holy Trinity at Rothwell, after it fell in 1660, and was eventually reinstated next to the tower.

6　The passage refers to a chalybeate spring discovered by Dr Richard Lower in 1614, which was to become the fashionable Astrop Spa, though later fell into decline. A replica well-head at St Rumbold's Well is set beside the road near to Astrop village.

7　In Abington Park, Northampton, built by William Thursby.

8　Depicted in a memorial stained glass window of St Andrew's Church at Great Cransley, subscribed by the 384th Bombardment Group of Grafton Underwood, an American outfit based there during World War II.

9　Marston Trussell.

10　Not necessarily: It signifies the gate 'kissing' the post, as on the Nene Way footpath at Flore and many other places.

18 ROYALTY

1　At the Cistercian Monastery at Pipewell, founded in 1143, where only bumps and humps remain visible.

2　Catharine Parr.

3　Fotheringhay Castle.

4　Wellingborough.

5　Elizabeth Woodville of Grafton Regis, on 1 May.

6　William Catesby, Speaker of the House of Commons, favourite of Richard III, buried in the church at Ashby St. Ledgers.

7　Brigstock.

8　Charles II, to help rebuild the town after the disasterous fire.

9　Whittlebury. In a document of Edward I (1272-1307), a piece of land is named as 'Dead Queen Moor'.

10　Mary Queen of Scots, beheaded 1587, is said to glide down the staircase at The Talbot Hotel in Oundle.

19 WRITERS AND POETS

1   Captain George Whyte-Melville.
2   John Dryden of Aldwincle.
3   Dame Edith Sitwell 1887-1964, Sir Osbert 1892-1969 and Sir Sacheverell 1900-1988.
4   In remembrance of her work as an author who devoted her writings to her innate love of the countryside.
5   Charles Dickens (1812-1870).
6   Prolific writer and naturalist 'BB', alias the late DJ Watkins-Pitchford, who latterly lived at Sudborough.
7   HE Bates, the quoted title was based on Rushden Hall.
8   John Clare 1793-1864, was a patient at Northampton Asylum (St Andrew's Hospital) for many years.
9   Thomas Randolph, who showed great promise in his career, but was distracted by the high life in London and died at the early age of 29 years.
10 George James de Wilde (1804-1871).

20 UNNATURAL CAUSES

1   George Tarry surprised the lovers and killed Theophillis Hart with a meat axe on 23 January 1685.
2   Captain Slash at Gallows Hill, Boughton Green.
3   Anthony Williams, in the graveyard of Holy Trinity church at Blatherwycke, trying to save Master O'Brien of the Hall.
4   Richard Knitter, at Bugbrooke.
5   Eleanor Shaw and Mary Phillips of Cotterstock, who were tried and found guilty of murder at Northampton Assizes in 1706, and were hanged and burned.
6   Running Rum was involved in a turf scandal and was buried at Sywell House.
7   Joe Adams and Jim Tyrrell from Silverstone suffered the ultimate penalty for their crime.
8   Isobel was the innocent victim, who learned of the killer's identity before the Court returned to the city after a visit to the country.

As the queen's coach paused at the ford where her lover was fatally attacked and slain, Isobel collapsed and died of a broken heart, in 1628.

9   Robert and Anne Stitchbury of Towcester, whose vicar, John Lockwood, was a staunch Loyalist. Robert took a hammer to his parish church and smashed the stained glass images of Christ and his followers. After his wife's painful demise, he became like a madman and inexplicably died soon after. His sister Anne thought that he had died as a result of the devil's intervention and tore and scattered the pages of her prayer-book in defiance. Soon beset with a mysterious disease, she was hounded from the town and left to die alone.

10   Andrew George Macrea, who had disposed of her head and arms in the warehouse and dumped the rest of her body in a ditch near Althorp Park railway station. He was found guilty at his trial and hanged in Northampton Gaol on January 10,1893.

21 ROGUES AND ECCENTRICS

1   Robert Catesby, in the Gunpowder Plot at Ashby St Ledgers.

2   Farmer Dunham of Hargrave.

3   'Watercress Harry' augmented his living by gathering and selling watercress. He was a well-known character in Kettering and had a local hostelry named after him, in Market Street.

4   Blakesley, by CW Bartholemew (1875-1919).

5   In the church at Sulgrave.

6   Whilton.

7   Josiah Eaton.

8   Mark Brewster, in the church of St Nicholas at Marston Trussell.

9   In 1840, John Dunkley was the keeper and victim, in Yardley Chase. The men were deported to Australia.

10   In the early hours of 6 November 1930, a burnt out car containing a male corpse was discovered at Hardingstone Lane, just outside Northampton. This sensational crime of that time, led to the arrest and eventual one-way trip to the gallows of Alfred Arthur Rouse, the accused.The victim is buried in an un-named

grave in Hardingstone churchyard.

22 FUR AND FEATHER

1 Lord Lilford, a leading ornothologist, of Lilford Hall.
2 Grundon, trained by Mr Bletsoe at Grendon Hall.
3 At Wicksteed Park, Kettering, to Jerry, the treasured pet of the founder, Charles Wicksteed.
4 Close to the gates of Sywell Country Park, in Washbrook Lane.
5 Lord Rothschild of Ashton Wold, near Oundle.
6 Spectral animals, some known as Black Dogs, sometimes of bizarre form, who in the past, have been said to haunt the Welland Valley.
7 Lady Knightley of Fawsley.
8 Gargoyles at Irchester Library.
9 The name from the 15th century indicating a rabbit warren.
10 The Reverend Thomas Jones, whose plight is illustrated in a stained glass window at All Hallows church at Wellingborough, riding on a bear.

23 CHURCHES

1 The parish church of St Mary at Rushden.
2 All Saints at Brixworth.
3 A female fertility symbol, one of four gargoyles on the tower of St Peter's Church at Isham.
4 The church of St Peter and St Paul at Easton Maudit.
5 All Saints Church at Braunston.
6 In the unique bone crypt beneath Holy Trinity Church at Rothwell, discovered in 1700, when medieval superstition dictated the saving of such bones for the Resurrection.
7 The church of St Mary Magdalene at Ecton and Holy Trinity at Hinton-in-the-Hedges.
8 St Mary's church on Combe Hill at Whiston, where the access is by field path only.

9   In Northampton. The church of the Holy Sepulchre, built by
Simon de Senlis, Earl of Northampton in 1100.

10   A human heart, probably that of Roger de Kirkton, who died in
1280 and was buried in Norfolk, but his heart was brought to
Woodford.

24 BATTLES AND SKIRMISHES

1   The churchyard of St Peter and St Paul at Kislingbury.

2   Holdenby House.

3   Subsequent to their arrest and trial at Northampton, the
prisoners were drawn and quartered, after the skirmish at
Newton-in-the-Willows.

4   Weedon Barracks at Weedon Bec was to be a stronghold for
George III against the anticipated invasion by the French at the
time of the Napoleonic Wars.

5   Easton-on-the-Hill.

6   Waterloo Covert at Arthingworth.

7   On the ground between Delapre Abbey and the River Nene.

8   Kilsby.

9   Rockingham Castle was held by the Roundheads until the end of
the war.

10   St Mary's, at Canons Ashby.

25 MONUMENTS

1   The Eleanor Cross at Geddington, one of only three of the
remaining original memorials, commissioned by Queen Eleanor's
husband, Edward I, after her death at Harby, Nottingham in 1290.
Each of the resting places of the funeral cortege en route for
Westminster Abbey, was marked in this way.

2   It refers to Charles Compton William Cavendish, 3rd Baronet
Chesham KCB, who died in a hunting accident on November 14,
1907.

.3   Naseby Obelisk was raised in 1936, as the earlier monument of

1823 was said to be wrongly sited. The Battle of Naseby of 1645, was the final clash of the Civil War, when the opposing armies of Royalists, under Charles I, were overcome by the Parliamentarian's New Model Army.

4   Erected by Sir English Dolben of Finedon Hall.

5   Charles Bradlaugh, whose statue was erected in Abington Square in 1894.

6   To Lt Percy Sinclair Pilcher, where momentoes of his career are displayed in an aviation museum, as he was a pioneer of early gliders.

7   The Market Square.

8   Second Earl of Strafford, at Boughton, in the 18th century.

9   The Round House or Wellington Tower, commemorates the Battle
     of Waterloo, by General Charles Arbuthnot of Woodford House. His guest, the Duke, remarked that the terrain, from this site, resembled that of the battle. A huge plaque reads 'Panorama Waterloo Victory June 18 AD 1825'. Once an inn, it is now privately owned.

10   To the 401st Bombardment Group (Heavy) of the 8th Air Force, based at Deenethorpe airfield from October 1943 to May 1945, when Flying Fortresses flew 254 missions over the war zones.

26 HERALDRY

1   Wellingborough. These represent Red, White, Stan, Burymoor and Rising Sun.

2   The Washington family.

3   Friendship is stronger than a castle.

4   Six seabird heads.

5   A falcon, bull and a hart.

6   William Knibb, who pursued the cause of slavery.

7   A scallop shell.

8   In church. They were often the coat of arms of a deceased person, specially painted for the funeral.

9   At Greens Norton — 'ER 1592'.

10   Morions, steel hats or head armour.

27 RAILWAYS

1   The Nene Valley Railway at Stibbington, near Peterborough or the Northampton and Lamport Railway at Pitsford and Brampton Station.
2   The Midland Main line, north of Wellingborough.
3   Harringworth Viaduct, with 82 arches, carrying the line between Kettering and Manton, opened in 1879.
4   Salcey Forest was used by passengers for only four months.
5   Higham Ferrers, where the nuts were gathered from the station's grounds.
6   On the outskirts of Thrapston.
7   Kilsby Tunnel, where Robert Stephenson was the line engineer.
8   Hunsbury Hill Museum at Northampton, East Carlton Park Heritage Museum, near Corby and the Irchester Narrow Guage Railway Museum at Irchester Country Park Near Wellingborough.
9   Bananas, carried from the docks at Bristol, to London.
10   The Great Central Line through Brackley and Woodford Halse in 1899.

28 MUSEUMS

1   At Ashton Mill, near Oundle (summer only).
2   The Heritage Museum at East Carlton Park, near Corby (open most days).
3   Earls Barton Museum, Barkers Yard, Station Road, Earls Barton (Saturdays only).
4   The Canal Museum, Stoke Bruerne (daily in summer, but limited opening in winter).
5   Abington Park Museum and Regimental Museum, in Abington Park, Northampton (open most days).
6   The Carpetbaggers Museum at Harrington (summer only).
7   Central Museum, Guildhall Road, Northampton (open daily).

8   The Heritage Centre, Croyland Hall, Burystead Place, Wellingborough (open most days).
9   Irchester Narrow Guage Railway Museum at Irchester Country Park. It is a tool designed to bend rail lines (open Sundays and bank holidays).
10   The Desborough Mirror. The emblem is on the cover of the *Northamptonshire Archaeology Journal*.

PICTURE QUIZ ANSWERS

1   Remaining wall of a columbarium or dovecote at Wilbarston.
2   Finedon Obelisk, erected by Sir English Dolben 'to record the many blessings of 1798'. At the crossroads.
3   Triangular Lodge in the grounds of Rushton Hall, built and completed by Sir thomas Tresham in 1597. (English Heritage).
4   Statue of Apollo Belvedere, mid-field at Blatherwycke, locally known as the Greek Archer.
5   Harringworth Viaduct, across the Welland Valley at Harringworth.
6   All Saints church at Brixworth, with Roman brick tiles. Said to the 'the oldest church north of the Alps'.
7   Wattle and daub wall at Flore, on the Nene Way.
8   Bone crypt beneath Holy Trinity church at Rothwell.
9   Scratch or mass dial on the porch of the church of St. Mary Magdalene at Ecton.
10   Ancient dovecote at Newton-le-Willows. with 2,000 nest boxes — late Elizabethan.
11   Beckets Well at Northampton.
12   Roman coffin lid, outside office block at Irchester Country Park, near Wellingborough.
13   Whilton, church of St. Andrew - a clock a bit short on minutes:
14   Vamping horn from Braybrooke (on loan to Market Harborough Museum).
15   Stocks near to the village shop at Little Houghton.
16   Old village pump at East Haddon.
17   Swan gates at Lamport Hall, emblem of the Isham family.
18   Lift bridge over the Grand Union Canal at Gayton.

19   Jim Crow tool for bending rail lines at the Irchester Narrow
      Guage Railway Museum at Irchester Country Park, near
      Wellingborough.
20   Market Cross at Higham Ferrers, on the Market Place; 14th
      century.

Front cover: St Mary and All Saints Church, Fotheringhay
Back cover: Triangular Lodge, Rushton